More Grade 3 Piano Solos

16 enjoyable pieces for Grade 3 pianists

GW00771406

Contents

Published by
Chester Music

Exclusive distributors:

Hal Leonard
7777 West Bluemound Road,
Milwaukee, WI 53213
Email: info@halleonard.com

Hal Leonard Europe Limited
42 Wigmore Street Marylebone,
London, WIU 2 RN
Email: info@halleonardeurope.com

Hal Leonard Australia Pty. Ltd.
4 Lentara Court Cheltenham,
Victoria, 9132 Australia
Email: info@halleonard.com.au

Order No. CH85261
ISBN 0-78558-364-3

Compiled and edited by Toby Knowels, Sam Lang and
James Welland.
Music arranged by Alistair Watson.
Music engraved and processed by Sarah Lofthouse, SEL
Music Art Ltd.

Printed in EU.

www.halleonard.com

Air
(from *Water Music*)

Music by George Frideric Handel

This is a good piece for practising dotted rhythms; they should help propel the music forward despite the slow tempo.

Ave Maria

Music by Franz Schubert

The hardest aspect of this piece is the rhythm, which switches between simple quavers and triplets.
A firm, steady pulse is essential. Keep both hands legato throughout, and try and 'sing' with your right hand.

Bills

Words & Music by Jacob Hindlin, Eric Frederic, Rickard Goransson & Gamal Lewis

Keep this moving along, but not too quickly.
Try not to rush the right-hand chromatic figure in the main riff.

Chim Chim Cher-ee
(from *Mary Poppins*)

Words & Music by Richard M. Sherman & Robert B. Sherman

It would be a good idea to practise playing thirds with your right hand before beginning this song.
Start the introduction very quietly. Try to bring out the top line in the right-hand chords.

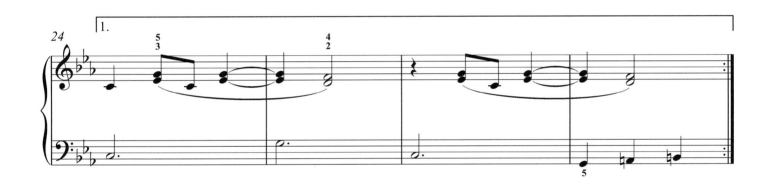

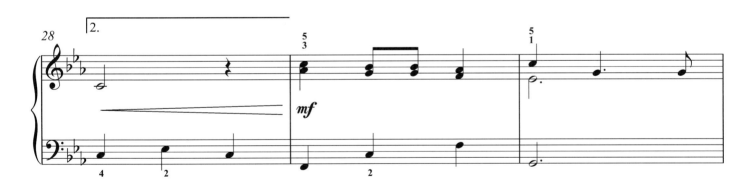

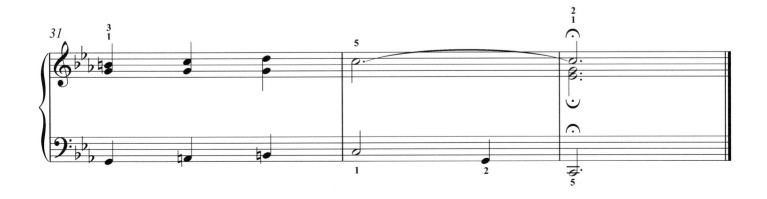

Nuvole Bianche

Music by Ludovico Einaudi

The first and last sections of this piece have a very different feel to the rest; try and create an atmosphere of stillness there.
The rest of the piece can be more flowing.

Frozen Heart
(from Disney's *Frozen*)

Words & Music by Robert Lopez & Kristen Anderson

Try and capture the cold atmosphere of this song.
Watch out for the 2/4 bars; keep counting crotchets.

Hard-working ($\quad$ = 80)

more urgency (♩ = 90)

Georgia On My Mind

Words by Stuart Gorrell
Music by Hoagy Carmichael

Enjoy the bluesy feel of this jazz standard. Take plenty of time; it should never sound rushed.
Aim for long, singing phrases in the right hand.

Moderately, with a blues feel (♩ = 90)

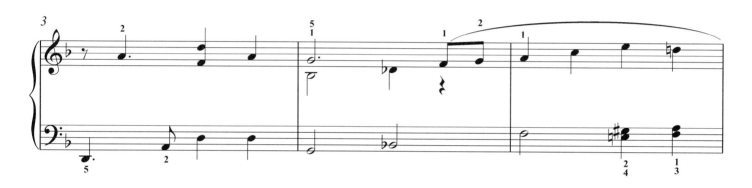

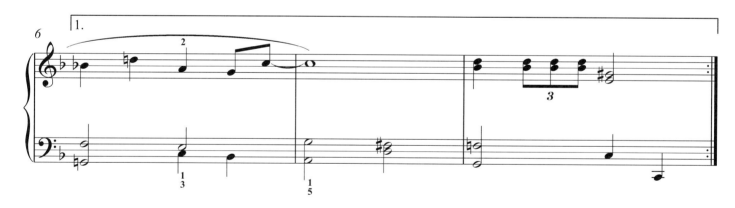

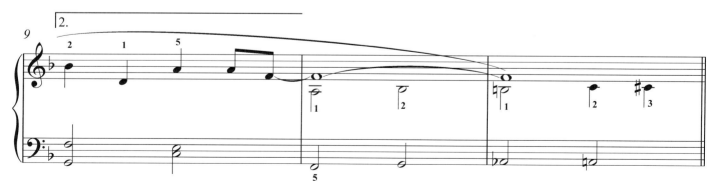

Hello

Words & Music by Greg Kurstin & Adele Adkins

This is a gentle song; start softly and slowly in order to fit in the right-hand semiquavers without rushing them.
The chorus on the second page should be noticeably louder.

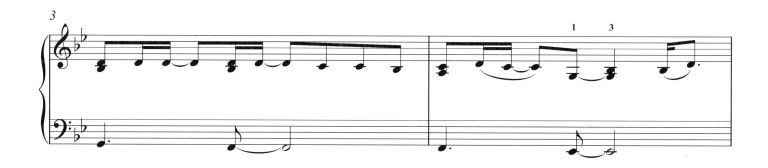

Jesu, Joy Of Man's Desiring

Music by Johann Sebastian Bach

In this piece the right-hand quavers need to be legato; they should flow seamlessly from one to the next.
The left-hand crotchets can be more detached.

Love Yourself

Words & Music by Benjamin Levin, Justin Bieber & Ed Sheeran

Try and make the right-hand phrases sound conversational at the beginning.
There's quite a lot of space in the left hand, so you will need to count carefully in the rests.
A strong sense of pulse is needed to deal with the offbeat rhythms from bar 25 onwards.

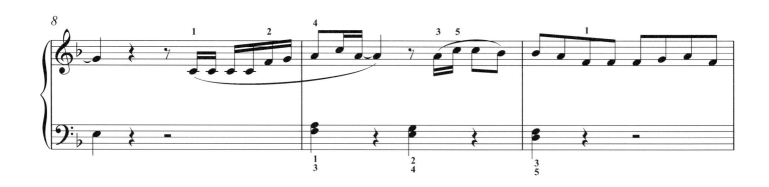

Naughty
(from *Matilda The Musical*)

Words & Music by Tim Minchin

The left hand stays staccato almost throughout this entire piece.

You need to be very confident with this hand, as the right hand has a lot of syncopation over the top of it.

Watch out for the changing time signatures and semibreve rests in bars 36 and 38.

Prelude in D♭ Major 'Raindrop'
(Op.28, No.4)

Music by Frédéric Chopin

There is a melancholy mood that you can try to bring out in this piece.

Keep it soft, gentle and simple; let the music speak for itself.

Be careful in bar 6 and again in bars 10 and 11 in the left hand. Follow the slurs here.

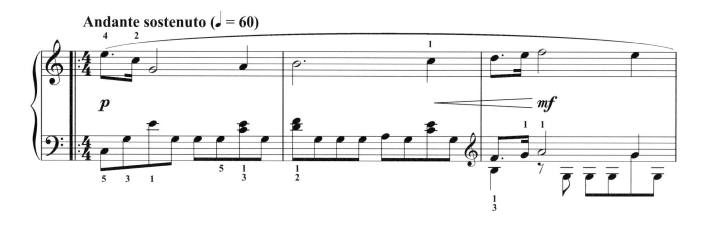

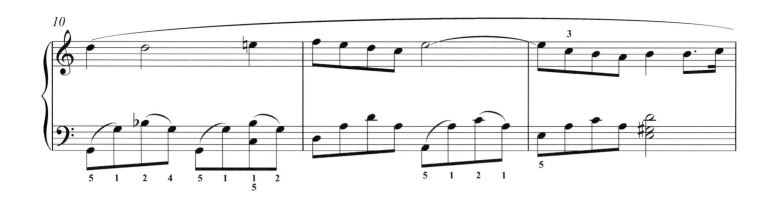

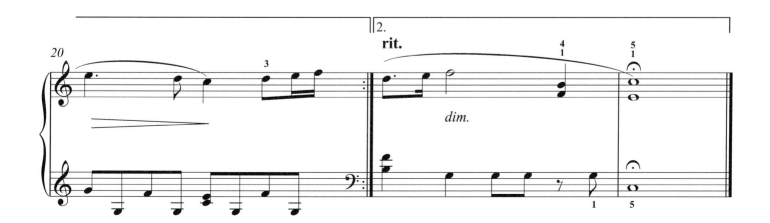

Paradise

Words & Music by Guy Berryman, Chris Martin, Jon Buckland, Brian Eno & Will Champion

Try to bring out the warmth in the harmonies of this song. Some pedal might help.
The technical challenge here is to hold down notes with your right-hand thumb while keeping the tune going over the top.

Pavane

Music by Gabriel Fauré

The staccato articulation in the left hand is best achieved by keeping a very relaxed wrist.
This will also help with the wide intervals required. The melody line needs to be very legato.

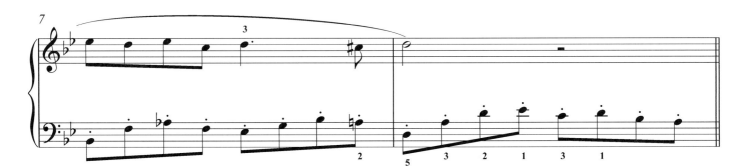

Writing's On The Wall

Words & Music by James Napier & Sam Smith

There are some big stretches here in the right hand. Carefully checking the fingering will help, as will the use of the pedal. Aim for a big dynamic range; remember you're trying to imitate an orchestra.

Waistband Dance
(from *Romanian Folk Dances*)

Music by Béla Bartók

This is a very quirky little piece. Don't worry if you can't manage the fast tempo marking;
it is still effective when played slower. Aim for crisp, short notes and chords.